Noumenon intellectual intuition) —
without aid of the senses).
monism beyond relativity — one
ultimate substance

Living in a Troubled World

Living in a Troubled World

Selections From the Writings of
William C. Menninger, M.D.

Edited by Bernard H. Hall, M.D.,
and Richard Rhodes

HALLMARK EDITIONS

Acknowledgments

Selections in this book are copyright 1931, 1940,
1942, 1947, 1948, 1950, 1951, 1952, © 1958, 1962,
1964 by The Menninger Foundation. Copyright
1947, 1954 by William C. Menninger, M.D.
All rights reserved.
This edition published by arrangement with
The Viking Press, Inc.
"Nervous breakdown..." reprinted from
Modern Hospital, January 1937.
"Wars begin in the minds of men..." reprinted
from *The Patient as a Person* (Chicago:
Department of Medicine and Religion, American
Medical Association, 1964).

Contents

Introduction

Dr. William Menninger, known affectionately by many as "Dr. Will," was a very lovable man. He was spontaneously interested in everyone he met, he served humanity, and when he died on September 6, 1966, one of the most distinguished physicians in the history of the United States left us forever. He was a loving husband and father, a devoted physician, and a national spokesman for the vital cause of mental health.

He loved life. Facing lingering illness, because he was a physician himself, he knew without being told by the physicians who cared for him that his days were numbered. Yet, from his sickbed at the Mayo Clinic, he responded to a note from me and ended the letter with a para-graph: "When I get home, let's take time for some fun—let's not fail to have some fun."

Fun! A man at the end of his life speaking of having fun! But he knew I would understand what he meant. For Dr. Will, life was fun—playing with his grandchildren, working with his stamps, or entertaining close friends. He had a secret about having fun which is also a secret of mental health. He undertook everything he did with zest and enthusiasm. Work was fun! He well knew that the difference between work and play is an attitude. For Dr. Will, "work" was play. I have known few men who worked as hard as he did—but he never thought of what he was doing as work. He did what he considered *important* to do—and because it was important, it became fun to do.

I thought of him often as Mr. Rhodes and I made the selections from his writings for this book. I am certain he would have gently heckled us with such remarks as, "Don't you fellows have anything better to do with your time?" or "What I have written isn't worth all that." But it would be only heckling. Because he would be delighted that we were doing something we considered important to do. It would not have mattered that the selections came from his own writings—that fact would be secondary to Dr. Will. Such was the magical love and concern for others which made him the man he was.

Dr. Will started his career as a physician in a small town in Kansas. He was a devoted physician and happy in his work. But fate was to intervene and change his life dramatically. Little did he realize when he began his medical career that he would become a missionary for the mentally ill and a psychiatrist for a troubled world. Paradoxically for a man of science, it was a world war that started the chain of events that led him to national prominence.

During World War II he was selected to be Director of the Neuropsychiatry Consultants Division of the Office of the Surgeon General. His responsibility was an awesome one: to care for the mental health of 10 million men, the entire Army of the United States. During the war two million men were lost to military service because of emotional problems. Undoubtedly this single fact convinced him that mental illness is our *number one health problem.*

He emerged from the war as a leader of American psychiatry, being elected the President of the American Psychoanalytic Association, the American Psychiatric Association, and the Group for the Advancement of Psychiatry, an organization which he founded. He traveled across the country teaching the principles of mental health to policemen, to housewives, to bankers, to clergymen, to fellow physicians — in fact, to any group that would listen to him. And many listened.

His talent as a national spokesman for the mentally ill was evident by 1953 when he was invited to speak to a state legislature about improved care for the mentally ill in that state. Subsequently, one governor after another asked him to speak to other legislatures, and during his career he spoke to a total of twenty-two. And then, in 1962, President John F. Kennedy asked to see him. The President was concerned about the mental health of the nation. Undoubtedly encouraged by his visit with Dr. Will, he sent in February of 1963 a message to the Congress of the United States which led to the passage of the National Mental Health Act.

Dr. Will's career began in a mortgaged old Kansas farmhouse which had been converted into a psychiatric hospital. Here, with his equally famous brother, Dr. Karl Menninger, and his father, Dr. Charles Frederick Menninger, he helped develop the Menninger Clinic which became widely known as a psychiatric treatment center.

The Menningers recognized that their small group practice of psychiatry could never have a significant impact on the national problem of mental illness. There were very few trained psychiatrists and other personnel necessary for the treatment of the mentally ill—clinical psychologists, psychiatric social workers, psychiatric nurses and attendants, and occupational therapists. The Menningers also knew that the research which had been done about mental illness was almost negligible. And because they were physicians, they were schooled in the conviction that it is the physician's obligation to learn how to prevent illnesses. They dreamed of a psychiatric center where not only could patients be treated but where psychiatrists and other mental health professionals could be trained. Their dream also included a research center and a department of preventive psychiatry.

To realize their dream of doing more about the national mental health problem, they decided in 1941 to incorporate the Menninger Clinic and Menninger Hospital as a nonprofit organization—The Menninger Foundation. When the Menninger Clinic was started in 1919 there were only three employees. The Menninger Foundation has grown to more than 900 employees who are devoted to four areas of attack on the nation's mental health needs — treatment, education, research, and prevention.

During the years that The Menninger Foundation was being developed Dr. Will always found time to write about his clinical experiences, his work as a teacher, and his belief in the cause of mental health. The selections from his writings published in this book will give the reader a sense of his breadth as a man.

Bernard H. Hall, M.D.

Living in a Troubled World

A Doctor's Life and Thoughts

Life is a flowing stream of opportunities, challenges, and problems which demand that... we adjust and readjust to them.

I'm a doctor. My lifework is medicine. There are many sad and tedious parts of it. But for me there's been great exhilaration and satisfaction in seeing sick people responding to treatment, from the feeling that I've had a little part in making life better for people who are in trouble. I've never felt that psychiatry, which is my specialty, can save the world all by itself. It presents no patent pill for ending war or meeting the threat of the atomic bomb—or even for getting children to stop biting their nails. Psychiatry, however, does help one understand himself better, and it helps us understand other people.

In dealing with emotional and mental illness, so much of the treatment process is concerned with the re-education of people and how they live their lives. In a sense, it is often a chance to teach them how to live more effectively.

I believe the world can be a better place to live in if people are healthier in their minds.

Let us define mental health as the adjustment of human beings to the world and to each other with a maximum of effectiveness and happiness. Not just efficiency, or just contentment — or the grace of obeying the rules of the game cheerfully. It is all of these together. It is the ability to maintain an even temper, an alert intelligence, socially considerate behavior, and a happy disposition. This, I think, is a healthy mind.

For maturity, everyone has to have a cause, a mission, an aim in life that is constructive and so big they have to keep working at it. For me, aside from medical missionary work in psychiatry, it's been Boy Scouting. But it can be almost anything. It's what satisfies the individual. Good causes with constructive opportunities exist in every community, for every age group, and on every level.

14

Psychiatry has not been considered very respect-able. There are many jokes about it, another evidence that it is not very well understood. The jokes are probably not unrelated to the lurking fear in the hearts of all of us that maybe there is something wrong with us and that we might need help sometime — and this we must deny!

The personality has many sides besides the emotional — the intellectual, the social, the voli-tional, the perceptual, and others. As we grow up, these various aspects of our personality should also develop, so that, ideally, we become a totally mature person. But what actually hap-pens (and it's easier to see in another person than in ourselves) is that we usually grow up in some areas of life but stay childish in others.

It's the other person who is a little bit queer. If three of us have been talking and one person leaves, he is just out of luck. Then as soon as you have left I decide that, if you did not have that awful mannerism, or if you did not talk so much, or if you were not so aggressive — well, you know what we say about each other.

As he explores his own subconscious, the patient in psychotherapy is like a fearful, struggling person who has come into an unfamiliar and totally darkened room crowded with furniture. He bumps into a chair and it falls over; he side-steps and hits a lamp, which crashes. He struggles against unseen, threatening enemies (the unconscious and therefore unknown forces in himself). With the gradual coming of light (the interpretations made by the therapist) the patient can see and evaluate those "threatening enemies" accurately. It then becomes his responsibility to put his house in order as he wishes.

Psychoanalysis is desirable for only a very small percentage of the patients who need psychiatric treatment. Like digitalis, or quinine, or any specific surgical procedure, psychoanalysis has a very specific set of indications and, therefore, a very limited use. Briefer and modified methods derived from psychoanalysis have, however, a much wider application.

"Psychoanalysis is amoral" is a criticism people raise. So, however, are surgery and medicine. It is true that an analysis may in some cases lead to divorce, or to less dependence on religion, or to a less rigid moral code. But when social, religious, or moral behavior patterns are part of an unhealthy, neurotic adjustment to life, they need to be changed. On the other hand, it is equally true that in many instances analysis may help the individual to gain far more satisfaction from his marital relationships, to find a more rational basis for his religious beliefs, and to achieve a really satisfying rather than a rigidly conforming personal way of life.

"Nervous breakdown" is a term used to include everything from headaches to fallen arches. Most often it is applied to those functionally incapacitated states in which the person is tired, nervous, weepy, and may have some secondary physical symptoms. But the designation of "nervous breakdown" is a misnomer, for almost never is there any disease or even disorder of the nerves. In almost every instance the sickness is more accurately a mental breakdown with associated physical symptoms — insomnia, upset stomach, tremulousness, fatigability, and others, all of which are partial expressions of the personality.

I suspect there are as many foxholes in civilian life as there were in military life. If we do anything at all in life that is worthwhile, sooner or later we find ourselves in an in-fighting spot in which we seem to be putting out so much energy and getting so little done. Under those circumstances it is wise to recognize that our mental health is not so good. Mental health is a matter of degree — of shades of gray, not black and white — and this principle applies to the most ill patient in a mental hospital or the most efficient president of a large corporation.

Although most professional people make their living by the use of intelligence, which may or may not be supplemented by the toil of their hands and the sweat of their brow, everyone makes his life through the emotions — through loves and hates, faith and hope, jubilations and disappointments. They are the vital part of life. We continuously react emotionally to the people and the things about us. Life is a flowing stream of opportunities, challenges, and problems which demand that, insofar as our capacity and our emotional response permit, we adjust and readjust to them. When an individual has emotional or intellectual or physical limitations the adjustment is more difficult. The difficulty is greatly increased when those about him lack an understanding of his situation.

Throughout life, if I've learned any one thing, it's been that it's not all in the books, that I've still got a lot to learn. Life—whatever your job—is a continuous growing process.

Are people today any more or any less happy than they were in more rigorous and primitive cultures or in other civilizations?

Has our progress in the field of pragmatic materialism blighted or minimized our aesthetic and spiritual values?

Have scientific, technical, and industrial developments, which have so greatly increased our material comforts, robbed many people of deep-seated satisfactions without offering suitable substitutions?

Have those great technological advances, which make it possible for us to defend ourselves against an enemy, stimulated man's instinctive, hostile aggressiveness beyond his capacity to handle it?

Is the resistance to change in human nature so great that anxiety has been aroused by the speed of our technological advance?

Such questions as these are raised because they are in the minds of all of us, but as yet no group has come up with an adequate answer.

On Marriage and Family Life

The most important single solution to our problems in family life is our potential capacity to care for each other, to love in the truest and broadest sense of that word.

What is it husbands and wives want, or should want? First, a partner who shares our life — including our sorrows and our joys, our failures and our successes. Second, the development of a home and life's richest reward — children. Third, a rich and rewarding personal life in terms of satisfaction, security, and achievement. Finally, to give some direction to our marriage as to whether it goes for "better" or "worse."

Perhaps the key to the marital relationship is how we handle our negative feelings toward each other. But to understand these there is a basic problem for all: very often the emotions may temporarily overrule the intelligence and judgment. All of us are at times guilty in varying degrees, but these aggressions can be corrected only if we are aware of them.

Husbands and wives must establish some priorities and objectives, really figuring out together what they want most in life and marriage and how they are jointly going to work toward these goals.

There must be a basic understanding of the role of each partner in relation to the other, and there must be some limits set and some compromises made. To achieve understanding, couples need:

1. Time to be alone, to think and talk together, without interruption.
2. A clear definition of the problem.
3. The opportunity to discuss alternatives.
4. Fifty per cent of each partner's time devoted to listening.
5. Compromises on what is "urgent" and what is merely "important."

These discussions can be aided by having a sense of humor; proper timing; not putting a partner on the defensive; not talking when too angry or upset; not letting the problem fester too long; and making a strong effort to understand what the other person is trying to say.

Our relationships in marriage depend so much upon our maturity. How effectively can we change and grow up from preferring to get to preferring to give? How much can we mature from loving ourselves, or getting love for ourselves, to giving love to someone else?

The most important single solution to our problems in family life is our potential capacity to care for each other, to love in the truest and broadest sense of that word, and to increase that capacity throughout life.

It seems to me that the alarming news we read of aggressor nations and power-hungry leaders is a corollary to those reports which point to the decrease in the home and family constructive influence. We are spending some 10 billions a year to combat crime in the United States, no small part of it for the care and correction of our more than 200,000 juvenile delinquents. The rate of divorce to marriage is now one to two in some parts of the country, one to three in other sections, and steadily increasing. In my opinion much of the world's sickness is due to home sickness, which can be cured only by the home remedy of family love, understanding, and cooperation.

The place above all others where children should receive love and thereby learn to love is in the family. One of the curses of our world is selfishness, and probably the only effective way to be rid of it is to begin with our children. They have to learn to love at an early stage, which means within the family group. Only through such an experience does anyone have a reasonable chance to develop social responsibility. Too often it is assumed that social responsibility is God-given. It is not. It has to be learned. It must be inculcated in children when they are very young. For most of us, only a rich family experience can help us attain sufficient emotional maturity to become more interested in others than in ourselves.

Emotional maturity in parents encourages emotional maturity in their children. It can be achieved by any family group that is ruled by council, not by edict; where the parents are genuinely interested in the things that interest their children, not patronizing; where responsibilities are shared by both the father and

23

mother, not shifted onto the back of one or shirked altogether.

These are the homes where there is open discussion of where the family will go on vacation or what movie they will see, and the children's votes are counted; where each and every member has his chores and responsibilities. These are the people who know that their family is — to paraphrase the proud soldier's comment about his fighting unit — "the best damn family in town," and that each one of them has a job to keep it so. And by the best family they mean that they have more fun together, less hostility, more sharing than any other family they know. These are the people who seldom if ever come to me as patients.

Society has given parents the task, the challenge, and the joy of caring for their babies, supervising their growth — and most important, loving them. Unfortunately, neither nature nor society automatically gives the necessary talent and knowledge to do the job that is a parent's.

There would be 100 per cent agreement among psychiatrists that the healthy development of the child depends on an early home situation that provides affection, good example, and security.

To the young man facing service in the military I would make four suggestions:

Accept the fact that you are going to be called on to serve your country; serve with pride.

Decide these are going to be rich years in your life; get every bit out of them you can.

Take advantage of every educational opportunity the armed forces offer; there are many.

Finally, get all you can out of the most important lesson you can learn: how to get along with all kinds of people. This means that you must learn to know yourself pretty well, and how to handle your frustrations. Learn how to make the most of bad situations, how to accept an occasional dictatorial sergeant—yes, even how to work occasionally under leadership which seems downright stupid. These are lessons of enormous value if you learn them well.

Another way of saying it is that, while the service isn't all pay and gravy, "the time is not wasted unless you waste it." What you get out of it you earn—and can keep.

On War and Peace

'Wars begin in the minds of men.' We should quickly add that this refers to your mind and my mind.

It is difficult, if not impossible, to classify the human activity of warfare in psychiatric terms. Such a pathological outpouring of aggression and destructiveness might well be regarded as a psychosis. The overt outlet of killing which the shooting war [World War II] provided is over, but one would need the utmost optimism to regard our present world status as any stage of convalescence. Nationally and internationally, our relationships are marked by tension, mistrust, suspicion, and selfishness. We cannot be unaware of the physical and emotional suffering that affects the majority of people in the world today, even though that suffering occurs thousands of miles from us. Our advances in physical science, as represented by the atom bomb and television, have progressed so much farther than our social advances that our very existence is dangerously threatened. We have learned how to eliminate space and to annihilate people, but we still lag far behind in learning to get along with each other.

There are few, if any, life situations in civilian existence that are comparable in their demands to the amount of readjustment that is required regularly in the army at war. The rude and abrupt separation from close personal ties to people and places by induction, which is followed by regimentation, discipline, lack of freedom, and the physical stress of training, is sufficient to produce personality disorders in many individuals. For those who survive this adjustment there await the demands of going to the far corners of the world, of living in extremes of climate, of doing battle with monotony, of having few or no recreational facilities, of experiencing repeated bombing attacks, and of having few of the comforts and none of the luxuries of previous everyday life. Finally, there is the supreme test of surviving the ordeal of combat, which certainly has no counterpart in civilian life.

[During World War II] in the "laboratory" of 10,000,000 soldiers and officers we learned many things that confirmed our theories about human behavior. We learned that leadership was by all odds the most important support we could give a man who was going into battle. We observed that many men with neurotic tendencies behaved well under good leadership and that many well-adjusted men under poor leadership went to pieces. For what we called leadership in wartime you can substitute confidence or trust or faith. It is what makes a man function well or badly. It is a set of qualities in the leader that can inspire men to tackle impossible jobs. If it is good enough, they will go to hell and back if requested to do so and not ask questions.

In civilian life it is supplied in some degree by the church, by teachers, by the football or basketball coach, and, most important, by the father and mother. We learned this too—leadership can never be a neutral thing. It is either destructive or constructive; it makes or breaks. Too often the fear with which children regard their parents is mistaken for the will to follow leaders, which only confidence inspires.

On America and war: The heritage and past history of America include a traumatic childhood with years of early struggle when it was literally a matter of the "survival of the fittest." Our nation started with economic poverty but spiritual wealth; it was founded on the determination to have freedom and liberty for every individual. In its later years a physical strength, unsurpassed by any other nation, has been developed, while its mental attitude has continued to be characterized by an ideology of freedom of thought, action, and speech, and a philosophy of "live and let live."

With all this strength, however, this nation of ours has manifested certain weaknesses. We, its people, have developed an illusion of being all-powerful. We are often accused of having made money our god. Certainly our wealth and power have so multiplied that the average individual has come to think that he must have a share merely because he is an American. Our freedom and liberty are believed to be things that are God-given, and too few of us have assumed our responsibility for earning and justifying our possession of them.

For many years, our relationship with the world was something of a paradox. We were primarily interested in the world for what it could bring us. Proportionately there have been few Americans with a world viewpoint, a desire for world brotherhood and equality, a desire that the whole world should develop in order that all men might prosper and live more richly. Far too many of us believed that America should assume an attitude which the psychiatrist sees in the schizophrenic patient, that of a withdrawal from the troubles of the world, a satisfaction and contentment within one's self, an atttude of "let the rest of the world go by." We developed a schism between our democratic ideals and our economic greed. Even in our own communities, most of us, most of the time, remain aloof or indifferent, while our political system is such that graft and greed can thrive.

With all of its weaknesses, which we physicians would regard as symptoms, we still believe that America is capable of surviving the disease War. If we can capitalize on the strongest assets of our heritage, our idealism, our economic and industrial strength, we can win.

"Wars begin in the minds of men." We should quickly add that this refers to your mind and my mind. We therefore need to recognize more clearly the evidences of hate in our own relationships — selfishness and resentment and prejudice and jealousy and bigotry — with the intent of more effectively controlling and reducing them. Simultaneously one must hope that each of us might increase our capacity for greater humility, that we might become more mature and hence give more of ourselves, and, in a broad sense, love more effectively.

These are the virtues that are cardinal in every religion and hence are the centers of interest of the rabbi and the priest and the minister in each of his parishioners. I happen to be one of those physicians who believes that these virtues are the center of our focus. In advocating this necessity to learn to love more effectively, one is mindful of the fact that every religion has taught us that God is love — and that it is from Him that one can gain strength — so well verbalized by the Psalmist: "I lift up mine eyes unto the hills from whence cometh my help." It is my conviction that this belief can be a bulwark of strength in the life of every one of us.

On Hobbies and Leisure Time

To the individual, good mental health is directly related to his capacity and willingness to play.

Mentally healthy people participate in some form of voluntary activity to supplement their required daily work. This is not merely because they want something to do in their leisure time, for many persons with little leisure time make time for play. Their satisfaction from these activities meets deep-seated psychological demands, quite beyond the superficial rationalization of enjoyment. The choice of activity is modified by their method of living and experience.

Too many people do not know how to play. Others limit their recreation to passive observation of the activity of others. Some people harbor the belief of our early forefathers that to play is sinful. Others feel that play is only for children and believe that "as I became a man I put away childish things." Some regard play as simply a waste of time as well as energy. Some consider play a reward for good behavior. Finally, some individuals have had such severe and rugged lives as children that they have never learned to play.

The psychiatrist is strongly in disagreement with all of these attitudes. There is considerable scientific evidence that the healthy personality is one who not only plays but who takes his play seriously. And there is also evidence that the inability and unwillingness to play reveals an insecure or disordered aspect of personality.

Some very concrete evidence of the relation between avocations and mental health was revealed in a survey made at our clinic some years ago. A group of well-adjusted individuals was surveyed as to the type, number, and duration of hobbies. The findings were compared to those from a similar survey of a group of psychiatric patients. In the well-adjusted group, both the number and the intensity of the pursuit of hobbies were far in excess of those of the patients. This doesn't mean that a hobby keeps an individual well. It does mean, though, that a well-adjusted individual learns how to play and does include play as an important feature of his life — much more frequently than does the average maladjusted person.

The word "recreation" refers to an enormous variety of human activity. What is the vocation of one man becomes the avocation of another. But the word generally refers to the things a person does for the fun of doing them, usually with no specific utilitarian or economic motive.

Such activity has a renewing effect psychologically. It is a re-creative experience. It enables a person to go back to psychologically unrewarding routine or work where the motivation is purely "to get the job done."

To the older person, recreation is an extremely important aid to growing older gracefully. People who stay young despite their years do so because of an active interest that provides satisfaction through participation.

The elderly person with a hobby is almost always an alert, interesting person. I can think of no more spectacular example than my remarkable physician father, who was an avid horticulturist and botanist all through his busy years as a physician. At the age of 75, when gardening became too strenuous, he became an expert in mineralogy, setting up his own machinery for cutting and polishing stones. At 85 he took up conchology — the study of seashells — and became proficient in identifying and classifying all types of *Mollusca*. At 90 he began the study of Braille.

By contrast, there is no more pathetic sight than the older person who has no interest in life and only sits and waits — vital evidence of the value of recreation to mental health.

Since life exacts a different toll from each of us, different sorts of recreation appeal to us. Psychiatrists cannot yet explain scientifically the psychological value of all types of activity, for obviously these must differ in considerable degree for different individuals. But there are at least three common psychological needs that are effectively met through participation in certain forms of recreation.

Competitive games provide an unusually satisfactory social outlet for the instinctive aggressive drive. It is a drive that constantly seeks expression in all of us. Where its direct expression is denied, symptoms may develop. There are perhaps specific values in varying degrees and types of competitive activity. The most aggressive outlet is seen in those sports in which there is bodily contact with an object, such as tennis, golf, badminton, bowling; and probably least, but still evident, in sports of primarily intellectual competition such as chess, checkers, bridge, poker, and so on. All these types of recreation meet the psychological need of many individuals whose jobs or daily work prevent sufficient expression of aggression.

Certain kinds of recreation offer the opportunity to create, bringing into use the other dominant instinctive drive of human beings — the erotic, constructive, or creative drive. Many individuals find great satisfaction in producing something — a rug, a chair, a piece of music, a poem, a cake.

Relaxation through entertainment also satisfies an important psychological need by allowing us to be passive and at the same time to participate vicariously. Many persons derive enormous satisfaction from listening to music, seeing a ball game or a movie, reading a mystery book, or studying art masterpieces.

By comparison with two generations ago, there is today a greater need for re-creative play.

People now have little opportunity to express their aggressive needs, to pioneer or to explore. Jobs, even though satisfying in most respects, provide a limited opportunity for spontaneous creativeness or a free choice of the type of activity.

Parents need to be educated about their role in their children's play. Ability to play is a learned ability. Therefore a child should have ample opportunity to play alone, to play with his parents, and to play with other children, both at home and elsewhere. It is not sufficient merely to send a child off to play in an isolated, make-believe world all by himself.

The child whose parents have avocational interests is much more likely to develop such interests. Not only is the example important, but the sharing of interests within the family is the source of much stimulation and satisfaction.

A word of caution: recreation is not like quinine, to be forced down the throat of the child. The child's interests should certainly not be restricted to those of his parents. The wise parent encourages the initial interests of his child as a serious, worthwhile endeavor, whether these be in sewing or lathe work, stamp collecting or baseball. Parents should not only set the example of participation in worthwhile activities, but also provide the facilities, the encouragement, and the approval of child-initiated activities.

To the individual, good mental health is directly related to his capacity and willingness to play. Regardless of his objections, resistances, or past practice, any individual will make a wise investment for himself if he does plan time for his play and take it seriously.

In this troubled world today, so filled with unhappiness, distress, anxiety, and restlessness, to whom can one look for help? It is my firm conviction that if we could encourage and teach and guide more people to more effective recreative activity, we could and would make a major contribution to our national and international peace of mind.

Over the Doctor's Shoulder

The most important medicine any physician ever administers is his own personality.

Beware of the pitfall which awaits all physicians, when and if they lose their sense of humility. It is a concealed trap because of the nature of the practice of medicine. As physicians we win the confidence of our patients and then accept responsibility for their lives. Our very acceptance of that relationship, however, often leads them to assume that we have knowledge or skill or power which we do not possess. They look upon us as the key to life or death. In a majority of instances they come to us with their hearts filled with fear. They assume — and often entirely correctly — that we are the *only* ones who can help them. Threatened as they are, they may give us physicians credit for far more ability or skill or knowledge than we have. Sometimes when nature is with us and we are able to live up to these great expectations, we then fall into that grievous error of permitting ourselves to think that we do have that ability or skill or knowledge. For a few moments we may dare to think we are as good as the patient thinks we are. My caution is to fight the illusion that we are as omniscient and omnipotent as our patients sometimes so strongly believe.

The physician must be a good listener. Sometimes he may need to guide the discourse, but to be sympathetic, patient, and understanding is essential. The patient wants to be heard even more than he wants to be seen. Unless he has ample opportunity to tell his story he is likely to be dissatisfied. And the telling of his story should not be regarded merely with indulgence or tolerance on the part of the doctor. It is of importance because, first, it is necessary for the physician to learn all he can about what his patient thinks and believes, how he feels, and why he thinks as he does. Second, the very act of telling his story to a sympathetic listener constitutes one of our most powerful therapeutic tools in medicine—mental catharsis. And, third, the very fact that the physician has devoted himself to the patient with sincere interest, and so indicated his respect for the patient and for his ideas, means that the physician has laid the cornerstone for building the confidence of that patient in the opinions and recommendations that he may later express.

Another admonition: I venture to discuss a very personal and intimate aspect of your life as a physician. Start on your career in medicine with the intention of making a life and not merely a living. Keep in mind that money can never buy the most priceless things that you desire. Chief among these is a rich family life. Many of you are married, and I hope all of you will be. The life of a young doctor is tough at best. During your internship and later in your residence training or in the military service, you must look forward to long hours of work away from home, which creates heavy odds against the establishment of a warm home life. No matter how demanding your medical career may become, you should plan deliberately with your wife to do what you can toward building a happy home life and a family. Nothing you will ever do will be more important.

Sometimes I think that the doctor has more obstacles to establishing a home life than the worker in any other kind of occupation. He has a code of medical ethics which prevents him from discussing his patients, thereby preventing the sharing with his family of that major aspect of his life. In fact, the young physician should explain this to his wife early in their marriage so that misunderstandings will not arise. Medical practice takes a doctor away from home so much, at such irregular hours, that his schedule is unpredictable, his energy for family and social activities very limited.

The most important medicine any physician ever administers is his own personality. This is most true in my specialty of psychiatry, where we must determine the dosage in the treatment of every patient. It is hardly less important in every branch of medicine.

The Challenge of Mental Health

Statistically, one out of every 12 of us, at some time during our lives, will spend some time in a mental institution.

So many people know little, if anything, about mental illness. Severe psychiatric illness often stimulates fear; sometimes repulsion; rarely does it arouse sympathy. Yet many families have a "skeleton in the closet" about which their members feel sensitive. Unfortunately, mentally ill patients are often stigmatized even after they are well.

Mental illness presents a tragic contradiction. No group of illnesses has a potentially higher rate of recovery. Most mental illness can be cured. In spite of this proven fact, however, mental illness continues to be the neglected hinterland, the great blind spot of all health problems confronting our nation today.

Statistically, one out of every 12 of us, at some time during our lives, will spend some time in a mental institution.

At any one moment, 52 per cent of all hospital beds in America are occupied by mentally ill people—a population of 750,000 souls! In too many of these public mental hospitals the great majority of the patients are badly neglected. Too many of these so-called hospitals are still human warehouses where we have put folks away.

Mental illness is the number one neglected health problem.

In considering the incidence of maladjustment, many surveys have shown that from 60 to 80 per cent of all dismissals in industry are due to social incompetence and only about 20 to 40 per cent to technical incompetence.

At least 75 per cent of accidents have a major psychological component in their causation. We could learn a great deal through research into the psychological component in accidents, but such studies are conspicuously lacking.

As the result of surveys of alcoholism we have learned something of its cost to business and industry. The problem drinker loses 22 days a year more than the average employee from the effects of his illness; he has twice as many accidents as the average person; he loses 12 years of his life span as compared with the nonalcoholic. It is understandable, therefore, that business refers to this situation as the "billion-dollar hangover."

The tensions in life for all of us manifest themselves in one way or another. Often we have regretted the bad judgment we used in this relationship or in that deal. In retrospect we wonder why we behaved the way we did. We can always see the problems in our associates and friends. The difficulty is to be able to see them in ourselves. Each time we look at the other fellow and see how queer he is, we would be smart to recognize that, at times, we are a bit difficult too. Our associates, and certainly our husbands or wives, will testify to this.

Emotional Maturity

The most mature person follows the adage of losing one's life to find it, a beautiful principle that was given to us more than a thousand years ago.

We all use the term "emotional maturity." We probably use it somewhat loosely. But there is a set of yardsticks we can use to measure how mature we are. And for me the ideal of good adjustment of life can only be reached by developing the many kinds of emotional maturity. So let's ask, and try to answer, the question, "What is emotional maturity?"

I have chosen seven standards that you can apply to your daily life and relationships with other people in order to judge how emotionally mature — how effective — you are. These could be subdivided into "57 varieties," but they're a good start.

Ability To Function Under Difficulty: The first measure of your maturity and mine is phrased as a question: *how well do you function when the going really gets rough?*

The world is full of buzz saws — hostility, selfishness, pettiness, suspicion, lack of understanding, witch-hunting, dishonesty, disappointment, and the losses we all suffer. These are part of reality. The small child can pretend he's anything he wants to be. Very severely ill mental patients can also ignore reality. But most of us go through daily experiences, often difficult to accept, which test us, sometimes severely. It's a question of how well we play the cards that are dealt us; some of us do it with very bad will at times, even though we partly choose the game we get into and the way we play it.

There are times when we want to run away, times when we do run away. We fail people who depend on us. We go to sleep or get sick or use many other devices to avoid responsibility. Sometimes we tear into situations, usually making them worse. We say there is nothing else to do but fight. This argument is the basis of war, the basis of crime. When we fight we disregard the situation and make our own rules.

None of these actions really resolves the problems. How able are we to come to a constructive compromise? Our capacity to accept reality depends upon how well we can accept frustration. All of us have friends who act on the childhood principle, "I want what I want when I want it." After a fashion some of them seem to get by—but most of us cannot. The fact is that anything worthwhile entails effort, and often requires us to delay satisfactions.

In our childhood some of us learned to accept frustration with minimal distress. Some were handicapped for life by not learning to be patient. Some were also handicapped by accepting frustration so completely that they lost all initiative. Accepting frustration is a hard lesson to learn, the more so for our children when we, as parents, do not help them realize that this is a rough world and that in it they cannot have everything that they want, or as much as they want, *when* they want it.

Dealing constructively with reality—functioning well under difficulty—means that we have learned a set of philosophical attitudes toward life and that we apply them in our family life. We are more concerned with what is in front of us than what is past. We try to direct our efforts toward realizable goals, hitching them to stars not too far out of our reach.

The better we are able to continue functioning

despite hazards and difficulties—and the more gracefully we do it—the greater is our maturity.

Capacity To Change: The second measurement of maturity is: *How flexible are you?* Do you have the capacity to change, knowing full well that the only certain thing in life is a continuing series of changes? We see so many people who become fixed, rigid. We get mad at them and call them stubborn. No matter what the new situation is, they do not change.

We need the capacity to grow with any situation in which we find ourselves. We must have enough vision to see what the possibilities are, and grow to accept the responsibilities those possibilities require if they are to be filled.

This applies particularly to our home life. One of the great handicaps many children suffer under is parents who will not change. These parents want to use the same methods that their parents used, forgetting that today is very different from yesterday. Television and automobiles are only two examples of developments that have created special parent-child problems.

As parents one of our great opportunities and responsibilities is to recognize that the world of our children is new to us. Can we adapt, adjust, and grow with it and with our children as they live through the difficult periods of childhood and teenage? And, incidentally, through the later years, for though our children are now adults I find I still have trouble keeping up with them. I recognize that if I get too rigid I shall lose them. I do not want this.

Lack of capacity to change — immaturity — is expressed when we try to solve the problems met as adults in the same way we did as children. Some of us are excellent pouters; some of us pick up our marbles and leave; some of us try to get on the slick side and do something fast. These are devices we should have outgrown long ago. They may have worked when we were five or six, but they do not work when we are adults.

Tension and Anxieties: The third measure of maturity is also a question: *how free are you from symptoms produced by tensions and anxieties?* I suspect that 80 per cent of our headaches develop from emotional problems. A very high percentage of stomach and intestinal upsets have emotional origins. The GI used to complain, "Oh, my aching back!" But we found during World War II that only about five per cent of the backs showed anything organically wrong. The individual had a problem, and he reflected his problem as a sore back.

It's helpful to remember that, at times, all of us are unreasonable. We are irrational; sometimes we are illogical; sometimes we use our physical symptoms as a club over those people we think we love. Tensions can appear as aggressiveness: people can be hard to get along with because they are so forward. They want to be in the center of the stage; they don't seem to know how conceited they are. They do not know how difficult they are to work with. They have to run the show or they will not be in the play.

On the other side of that coin are those who are so passive that they go through life hanging onto somebody's apron strings. It's the only way they know how to get there. And such passivity can also be the strongest kind of aggression that anybody can use. These people are the wet-blanket throwers, the people who say, "for God's sake, let's do something," and then forget the whole business. These are people whose passivity conceals their aggression.

Other people are too shy. They would like to get into the swim and be like the rest of us — or at least they feel they would — but they walk along on the bank and watch, because they are afraid.

Others hate authority. Their childhood experiences at home make them leave home hating all authority.

As we see these troubled people we are usually too thoughtless to try to understand their problems, which stem from early family experience. We rationalize their problems away, finding explanations that make sense to us even though they make no sense to anyone else. "My mind is made up, don't confuse me with the facts," we say in effect. All prejudices are rationalizations, and all rationalizations are bluffs.

How many times do we try to bluff each other? Some of us rationalize entirely too much, whether on the job, at a bridge game, or in the kitchen. "It isn't my fault, it's your fault, and everything that goes wrong is your fault." It looks as if one of the advantages of marriage is to have a scapegoat. We can blame our problems on our spouse when the going gets too rough. It's convenient, of course, but it's also evidence of our immaturity.

To Give Rather Than Receive: Another important measure of maturity is *the capacity to find more satisfaction in giving than in receiving.* We start out as infants with everything coming our way. Many of us would like to continue playing that nice, happy, blissful role all of our lives, and an amazing number of us try to do just this. But to grow up, the role must be reversed: instead of being on the receiving end the mature person is on the giving end of the line.

None of us ever give up all our pleasure in receiving. We like to receive, and we should. But I hope we go far beyond that to find our greatest satisfaction in giving of ourselves to our children, to our communities, and to the social needs of this shrinking world in which we live.

The most mature person follows the adage of losing one's life to find it, a beautiful principle that was given to us more than a thousand years ago. It is a mental health practice to find a mission that is so much bigger than you are that you can never accomplish it alone, a mission for the common good, a mission that takes thought and energy.

Harry Emerson Fosdick defined a real person as an individual who stands out because of his social conscience, because of what he has done for his fellow men, what he has given of himself. This is part of emotional maturity, and I would strongly urge that if you have no mission, find one.

Getting Along With Others: Everything I've said so far implies another question of emotional maturity: *how well do you get along with other people?* How do you relate to your wife? your husband? your children? There is much evidence that many of us do not relate very well. Witness the number of broken homes, the number of law-breakers, the amount of scapegoating and witch-hunting, the amount of bickering and sniping between groups of us — social, racial, economic, political, and religious. We don't have to look far to see that in our international relations we do not seem to understand each other very well either. What is your personal capacity to relate to other people and how well do you do it?

There seem to be people who operate by wanting to make other people unhappy, mean folks who seem to derive satisfaction in venting their hate on the rest of us. Tragically, too often in clinical work the psychiatrist sees this attitude in parents with children, in employers with employees, in schoolteachers with pupils, in all categories where we must live with others.

How does one test sincerity? Where did it come from? How does your child become a sincere or an insincere person? Where does one get integrity? We can feel these attributes in each other, but I do not know of any test for them. Yet they are vital for healthy personal relationships. Would that all of us could learn how to develop these characteristics! It is not easy, but the recognition that we ought to be better persons is, I think, the first step toward getting there.

Hate and Guilt: Our major problem in life concerns my next point: *how do you handle your hate?* In all of us there is an instinctive tendency — unless curbed, unless neutralized — to hate. We cannot be unaware of the enormous amount of hate, suspicion, and fear in our world.

Sometimes we turn it on ourselves. We are not kind and thoughtful, and then, with some justification, though often futilely, we hate ourselves. We feel guilty. Guilt never exists without hate, hate that has been felt or expressed. At times we all have recognized at least the guilt, if not the hate. Too often we arrange for self-punishment for ourselves. We know we are capable or competent but we fail ourselves. The most dramatic self-punishment is when a man kills himself.

Hate is often turned on the family. Various disguises of hostility are used by man and wife, in terms of thoughtlessness and selfishness. We do not consider the other spouse's thinking, wishes, and hopes. We often shun family responsibilities. We express hostility toward our children by getting so interested in ourselves that we don't have much time for them.

How often we turn hate on our associates, people whom we call our friends, and about whom we say we care a great deal! It is truly a challenge to "love thy neighbor as thyself." Would that we could be so mature! Certainly we can try.

Many people, in an indefinite way, turn their hate on society as a whole, by their lack of any sense of responsibility. They do little for their communities. Some disturbing statistics about executives bring this point home. Forty-six per cent of those studied had no extracurricular activity, which means that they had no community activity. What is yours?

Hostility is expressed by people who are stingy, who do not give of themselves or their substance or their time to the causes that have to go forward.

If only we would sublimate our hostile feelings into creative, constructive outlets — and we can! We can in our community, in our family life, by turning our energy into cultural, intellectual, and recreational activities. Work — work is one of the best kinds of sublimation for one's hostility. Not by chance have we developed the old principle of going out behind the barn to whittle a while when angry instead of expressing the anger directly against someone else. Hate is the root of all mental illness; it is the root of the problems of our world. It reveals itself in the emotional responses of each one of us. If we would just learn how to control it!

The Need to Love: What can we do about hate? Along with the instinctive drive to hate, *we also have an instinctive drive to love.* It must be allowed a chance to express itself. The only neutralization we know for hate is love, love in the broad sense, love that makes me want to do something constructive rather than destructive. This business of learning how to love is probably the most important lesson anyone ever learns in life, if he is fortunate enough to learn it.

My point is that all of us can do a better job of learning this lesson. Some of us were fortunate enough to have parents who cared about us, who loved us, and who thereby taught us to love them in return. That love was then expanded beyond our immediate family circle to include neighbors and associates in the community, the city, the state, the nation, and hopefully the many people in our world. We learn to care because we love, and that alone makes us constructive and neutralizes the hate that is in the soul of all of us. It is my conviction that the hope of the world must rest on enough people becoming mature enough to love.

I hope that you will use these measures of

maturity in making an honest effort to look at yourself for a minute. I hope then that all of us will try to be a little more mature. I hope we will try to raise children who are more mature than we are. Above anything else, I hope all of us give ourselves the opportunity to express the love that we have, to reduce, in some small way, the hate in the world around us.

Certainly the world could never before have had more grief and unhappiness and human turmoil than currently exists. We—you and I— must assume some responsibility for reducing this turmoil. We have made such remarkable technological advances that we have become proficient in building great cities and the most complicated gadgets. We dare not continue letting our inability to get along with each other destroy our cities, our gadgets, ourselves. What gain to be scientific geniuses if we remain social imbeciles? The responsibility for achieving social and emotional maturity—which in turn depends upon preventing and treating mental ill health— lies entirely with you and me. What will you do about it?

The Menninger Foundation

Established by Doctors William and Karl Menninger, the Menninger Foundation of Topeka, Kansas, is a world-renowned center of diagnostic and treatment services for adults and children, professional training for psychiatrists and other mental health personnel, research into human behavior, and pioneer studies in improving mental health.

Dr. Bernhard H. Hall, the primary editor of this book, is director of Out-Patient Services for the Foundation's Clinic.

Living in a Troubled World

Designed by J. William Burdett.
Set in Palatino, a 20th century typeface
resembling a Venetian, designed by
Hermann Zapf of Frankfurt.
Printed on Hallmark Eggshell Book paper.